P9-DCA-586

PREP
(PREPARATORY)
LEVEL

# *Getting the Main Idea*

*RICHARD A. BONING*

Third Edition

Text Revision by Brown Publishing Network, Inc., Wellesley, Massachusetts

Project Design, Art, and Cover by The Quarasan Group, Inc., Northbrook, Illinois

Barnell Loft Supervision
   John Higgins, Editor in Chief
   Estelle Kleinman, Senior Editor
   Barbara Knight, Product Development Director

## PURPOSE:

GETTING THE MAIN IDEA is designed to assist pupils in grasping the central thought of a short passage. This skill is not only one of the most important of all major skills, but one which must be developed from the earliest stages.

## FOR WHOM:

The skill of GETTING THE MAIN IDEA is developed through a series of books spanning ten levels (Picture, Preparatory, A, B, C, D, E, F, G, H). The Picture Level is for pupils who have not acquired a basic sight vocabulary. The Preparatory Level is for pupils who have a basic sight vocabulary but are not yet ready for the first-grade-level book. Books A through H are appropriate for pupils who can read on levels one through eight, respectively. **The use of the *Specific Skill Series Placement Test* is recommended to determine the appropriate level.**

## THE NEW EDITION:

For this new edition Barnell Loft has not only replaced or updated a number of selections but has also emplaced all new art and added an entirely new feature, **Integrated Language Activities** ("L A P"—Language Activity Pages—is its title). This consists of four two-page sections following Units 6, 12, 19, and 25 (on the Picture, Preparatory, and A levels, Units 12, 24, 38, and 50). Each section has four parts: Exercising Your Skill, Expanding Your Skill, Exploring Language, and Expressing Yourself. These pages lead the pupil beyond the book through a broadening spiral of writing, speaking, and other individual and group language activities that apply and extend the skill being developed. Many of these activities involve open-ended thinking and expression. It is the teacher's option to use all, some, or none of the activities in any section (though some activities depend on preceding ones).

Another addition on each level is an **About This Book** page, which explains the skill to pupils and shows them how best to approach the reading selections and questions.

On the lowest levels, pupils should have About This Book and many parts of the Language Activity Pages read to them.

## SESSIONS:

Short practice sessions are the most effective. It is desirable to have a practice session every day or every other day, using a few units each session.

## SCORING:

Pupils should record their answers on the reproducible worksheets. The worksheets make scoring easier and provide uniform records of the pupils' work. Using worksheets also avoids consuming exercise books.

It is important for pupils to know how well they are doing. For this reason, units should be scored as soon as they have been completed. Then a discussion can be held in which pupils justify their choices. (The Integrated Language Activities, many of which are open-ended, do not lend themselves to an objective score; thus there are no answer keys for these pages.)

## GENERAL INFORMATION ON *GETTING THE MAIN IDEA:*

There are several ways by which teachers can help pupils identify main ideas.

A. **Topic Words:** Pupils tell in a word or two the topic of the paragraph.

B. **Key Question Words:** Pupils learn that questions can begin with special words: *Why, Where, When, How,* and *What.*

C. **Place Clues:** Pupils become aware of paragraph structure. They learn that the main idea is often stated in the first or last sentence.

D. **Space Clues:** Pupils learn that the central thought of a paragraph is not limited to a single sentence, even though it may be stated in one sentence.

E. **Turnabout Clues:** If the main idea is stated in one sentence, pupils learn to change that sentence into a question and see if the whole paragraph answers it.

F. **General and Specific Ideas:** Pupils understand that some words are more general or inclusive than others. Pupils compare sentences to determine which are more inclusive and which are supporting sentences.

## SUGGESTED STEPS:

1. Pupils read the passage. (On the Picture Level, they look at the picture.)
2. After reading each passage (or looking at the picture), the readers select its main idea. The choices are on the opposite page (or below the picture/passage, at the Picture, Preparatory, and A levels).

Additional information on using GETTING THE MAIN IDEA with pupils will be found in the **Specific Skill Series Teacher's Manual.**

## RELATED MATERIALS:

**Specific Skill Series Placement Tests**, which enable the teacher to place pupils at their appropriate levels in each skill, are available for the Elementary (Pre-1–6) and Midway (4–8) grade levels. Titles of the complete **Specific Skill Series**, available on the same levels as GETTING THE MAIN IDEA, are listed on the back cover.

# About This Book

A picture or a story is about something. It has a subject. Read this story. Think of what the story is mainly about.

A boy is running. A girl is running. They are having a race.

The first two sentences tell about certain parts of the whole story. They are **details**. The last sentence tells what the whole story is mainly about. A sentence that tells what the whole story is mainly about is the **main idea**.

You can think of a main idea as being like a tree. A tree has many parts. It has a trunk, roots, leaves, and branches. All these parts together add up to make a whole tree. They are like the details in a story. The details add up to make the main idea.

Sometimes, the main idea is in a sentence in the story. The last sentence of the story above tells the main idea. Sometimes, there is no main idea sentence. Then you have to ask yourself, "What is the story about?"

Read this story. Think of what it is mainly about.

Jeff brushes his dog's fur. He gives his dog fresh food and water. He takes it for long walks.

This story tells only about details. You can guess that the main idea is "Jeff takes good care of his dog." All the details tell about this main idea.

In this book, you will read stories and look at pictures. Think about the details in each story. Ask yourself, "What is the story *mainly* about?" Then choose the sentence that tells the main idea of the story.

Rosa could not find her hat. She looked and looked. Then Rosa saw her cat. The cat was sleeping in her hat.

---

What is the main idea?

**(A) The cat wanted to play.**

**(B) Rosa found her hat.**

Father was going fishing. "Good-by. I will be back in two days," he said. Father got into his car. The car went down the street.

---

What is the main idea?

(A) **Father came home.**

(B) **Father went away.**

Betty looked out the window. It was raining. She could not go out to play. Betty said, "I wish it would stop raining."

---

What is the main idea?

**(A) Betty wanted the rain to stop.**

**(B) Betty liked looking at the rain.**

Tom got out of the car. He took a picture of the falls. The water went down, down, down over the rocks.

---

What is the main idea?

(A) **Tom saw rocks fall over the top.**

(B) **Tom took a picture of falling water.**

The dog could not walk. Maria took it into her house. The dog stayed at Maria's house for five days. Then it could walk again.

---

What is the main idea?

(A) **Maria helped a dog.**

(B) **A dog ran away.**

Amy said, "I wish I could find my book." She looked for the book at school. She looked in her house. But Amy could not find it.

What is the main idea?

(A) **Amy got a new book.**

(B) **Amy could not find her book.**

Rick went to a farm. He saw two goats and a pig. He saw a big horse. Rick said, "I want to come back to the farm again."

---

What is the main idea?

**(A) Rick saw a pig.**

**(B) Rick liked the farm.**

Last night, the girls looked at TV. They saw a show about a pig. It was a fat pig that liked to eat. The girls had a good time.

---

What is the main idea?

**(A) The girls saw a pig on TV.**

**(B) The girls had something to eat.**

Bill got on the bus. He was going to see a friend. Bill was on the bus for five days. He was happy when the ride was over.

---

What is the main idea?

**(A) Bill took a long bus ride.**

**(B) Bill had fun on a bus.**

"Try to get me," called Ann. She ran down the street. Her friends ran after Ann, but they could not get her. Ann was too fast.

---

What is the main idea?

(A) **Ann has many friends.**

(B) **No one could get Ann.**

School is over. Now the children will have fun at the park each day. They will swim and play ball.

What is the main idea?

**(A) The children are sad when school is over.**

**(B) The children like to do things at the park.**

Jack was playing ball. When he went home, he did not take his coat. Jack went back to look for his coat. It was not there.

---

What is the main idea?

(A) **Jack found his lost coat.**

(B) **Jack lost his coat.**

## A. Exercising Your Skill

The children in the picture are going to the park. Be a detective. Search for main idea clues in the picture. Look at the picture carefully. On your paper, answer the questions below.

1.  Where have the children been?
2.  Why are they smiling?
3.  Why do the children like to go to the park?
4.  Give the picture and story a name. The name should be the main idea.

## B. Expanding Your Skill

Read the lists below. Write names for each list. The names should tell the main idea of each list.

### At the Park

| _____ | _____ |
| --- | --- |
| play ball | swings |
| jump rope | slide |
| ride a bike | bench |

## C. Exploring Language

Write the story on your paper. Use your own words to fill in the blanks. Then give the story a name. The name should tell the main idea.

What do I like to do after school? When I get home I like to ____. Then I spend time in my ____. Sometimes I ____ books. Sometimes I play with my ____.

## D. Expressing Yourself

Do one of these things.

1. Draw a picture of you doing something fun at the park. Give the picture a name.

2. Write what two children might talk about as they walk to the park. Have them talk about what they will do at the park. With a friend, act out what the children say. Give this little story a name.

A cow was walking down the street. Mary was sitting on the cow. She was taking the cow to her father's farm. It was funny to see Mary on the cow.

---

What is the main idea?

(A) **Father has a cow.**

(B) **Mary was riding a cow.**

"May I have some more cake?" asked Tom. Mother gave him more cake to eat. Tom was happy. His mother made a good cake.

Betty got a new wagon. She sat in her wagon and went down a hill. It was a long hill. Betty went very fast.

What is the main idea?

(A) **Betty had a fast ride.**

(B) **Betty gave her wagon away.**

Mother gave Peg a book. It was a book about animals. Peg took it to bed with her. She read the book before she went to sleep.

What is the main idea?

(A) **Mother likes to read.**

(B) **Peg read in bed.**

There were many children at Rick's party. They played games and had cake to eat. Then the children gave Rick a surprise. It was a toy airplane.

---

What is the main idea?

(A) **Rick made a cake.**

(B) **Rick had a party.**

24

When Father made a table, Bill painted it. After Father cut the grass, Bill put water on it. Father likes to have Bill help him.

---

What is the main idea?

**(A) Bill helped his father.**

**(B) Bill got a new table.**

Mother was going to see a friend. She did not know if she should go on a bus or a train. At last Mother said, "I will go on a bus."

---

What is the main idea?

**(A) Mother will take a bus ride.**

**(B) Mother will take a train ride.**

Ted looked up. There was a big bird flying over his house. It was flying very high. Ted said, "I wish I could fly like a bird."

---

What is the main idea?

**(A) The bird was very small.**

**(B) Ted would like to fly like a bird.**

"Tell us a story," said the girls. Mary told them about a funny pig. The pig hopped like a rabbit. The girls liked Mary's story.

---

What is the main idea?

(A) **Mary has a pet.**

(B) **Mary tells a story.**

"I hear the baby crying," said Jenny. She went to look at the baby. It was crying. Jenny gave the baby something to eat. Soon the baby was sleeping again.

---

What is the main idea?

(A) **Jenny helped a crying baby.**

(B) **Jenny found a lost baby.**

Some flowers need more light than others. Some flowers need more water than others. All flowers need food to help them grow.

What is the main idea?

(A) **Flowers need water every day.**

(B) **Flowers need light, water, and food.**

Mary ran home from school. She wanted to ride her bike. Mary put her books in the house. Then she went riding down the street on her bike.

---

What is the main idea?

(A) **Mary likes riding her bike.**

(B) **Mary likes going to school.**

## A. Exercising Your Skill

Look at the picture. Then read the words in each list below. On your own paper, write a good name for each list of words.

On a Farm

| | |
| --- | --- |
| cows | barn |
| sheep | fence |
| pigs | tractor |
| horses | crops |

## B. Expanding Your Skill

Talk about the picture.

1. Where does the picture take place?
2. Which animals do you see in the picture?
3. What is a good name for the picture? The name should tell the main idea.

## C. Exploring Language

Write the story that follows on your paper. Use your own words to fill in the blanks. Give the story a name. The name tells the main idea of the story.

Did you ever visit a farm? There are many different kinds of animals on a farm. A ____, ____, and ____ live on a farm. Some of these animals sleep and eat in a ____. It is a place where animals can stay warm.

## D. Expressing Yourself

Do one of these things.

1. Draw a picture of something you would like to see on a farm. Write a sentence that tells about why you would like to see it.

2. Pretend to be an animal. Move like it. Make sounds like it. See if your class can guess the animal. Give word clues to tell about the animal if you need to.

It was Bill's birthday. He got a toy train and a toy truck. He got a toy car too. Bill said, "I like having birthdays."

---

What is the main idea?

(A) **Bill got toys for his birthday.**

(B) **Bill went to a birthday party.**

Mother gave the children a new game. The children played the game all day. The next day, they stayed in the house. They wanted to play the game again.

---

What is the main idea?

(A) **The children liked the game.**

(B) **The children could not go out.**

When Susan got out of school, it was raining. She ran all the way home. Susan ran fast, but she still got very wet.

What is the main idea?

(A) **Susan went to school.**

(B) **Susan ran home in the rain.**

Tom was playing with his dog. A cat ran by. Tom's dog ran after the cat. The cat went up a tree. Tom's dog could not go up the tree.

---

What is the main idea?

(A) **A cat got away.**

(B) **Tom found a cat.**

"We do not have any food," said Mother. Maria got on her bike and went down the street. Soon she was back. She gave Mother a bag of food.

---

What is the main idea?

(A) **Mother gave Maria a bike.**

(B) **Maria got food for Mother.**

38

Gary wanted to take his dog in the car. Father said, "The dog has to stay home." Gary wanted to stay home too, but his father would not let him.

What is the main idea?

**(A) Father and Gary had fun.**

**(B) Gary's dog stayed home.**

Ann's friends came to her house. She made a cake. The girls began to eat the cake, but they stopped. No one wanted to eat Ann's cake.

---

What is the main idea?

**(A) No one liked Ann's cake.**

**(B) Ann's friends liked her cake.**

Linda went away in her old car. When she came back, she was in a new car. Linda asked her mother, "How do you like my new car?"

---

What is the main idea?

**(A) Linda gave Mother a ride.**

**(B) Linda showed Mother her new car.**

Do you laugh when it rains? You are right to be happy. If no rain comes down, there is no water for people to use. People need water.

---

What is the main idea?

**(A) Rain helps people.**

**(B) Rain makes the plants grow big.**

Mary said, "I can jump over the water." Mary ran and jumped, but she went into the water. When Mary went home, she was very wet.

---

What is the main idea?

(A) **Mary jumped into the water.**

(B) **Mary can jump far.**

The balloon went out of Jim's hand. Up, up it went. It went far away. Jim wished he still had the balloon. It was fun to play with.

What is the main idea?

**(A) Jim did not like the balloon.**

**(B) Jim lost his balloon.**

"Please help me read this story," said Pam. Mother sat next to Pam. Mother told her the words she did not know. Pam liked reading with Mother.

---

What is the main idea?

(A) **Mother helped Pam read.**

(B) **Pam found a book.**

"My cat does funny things," said Betty. "It sleeps in my hat. It plays with my toys. I like looking at my funny cat."

---

What is the main idea?

(A) Betty is a funny girl.

(B) Betty's cat does funny things.

The grass around Tony's house was not green. Tony put water on the grass. The next day, he put more water on the grass. Soon the grass was green.

---

What is the main idea?

(A) Tony played on the grass.

(B) Tony helped make the grass green.

## A. Exercising Your Skill

Look at the picture carefully. What is the main idea? Write the word map below on your paper. Write the main idea of the picture in the middle circle. In the other circles, list the things you need for baking.

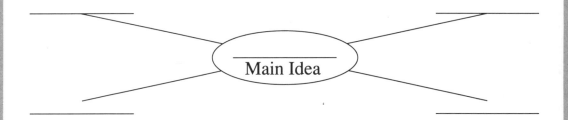

Main Idea

## B. Expanding Your Skill

Do you like to bake? Read each list of words below. On your paper, write a good name for each list.

| _____ | _____ |
|---------|---------|
| cookies | bowl |
| bread | oven |
| pie | measuring cup |

## C. Exploring Language

Here are some steps for baking one kind of bread. On your paper, fill in the blanks. Then give the recipe a name. The name tells the main idea.

Put the flour, yeast, water, and salt into a large _____.

Stir until the batter is _____.

Put the batter in a bread pan and bake it in a warm _____.

## D. Expressing Yourself

Do one of these things.

1. Pretend you write about food for a newspaper. Ask Ann for her cake recipe. Be sure to give it a name.

2. Pretend you are the judge at a baking contest. Tell about all the different cakes. Write about how you would pick the winner.

Father was riding in a train. He was in the train for three days. At last, the train stopped. Father was happy to be home.

What is the main idea?

(A) **Father came home in a train.**

(B) **Father went away in a train.**

Mary found a book in the street. She took it home to show Mother. Mother said, "That is my book. I must have dropped it."

___

What is the main idea?

**(A) Mary read a good book.**

**(B) Mary found Mother's book.**

Bill got a new boat. Tom got a new boat too. Bill and Tom went fast in their boats. They wanted to find out which boat was faster.

---

What is the main idea?

(A) **Bill likes the water.**

(B) **The boys had a boat race.**

Ann was going to bed. She saw a big box by her bed. There was a surprise in the box. It was a new TV for Ann.

---

What is the main idea?

(A) **Ann got a new TV.**

(B) **Ann went to bed.**

A cat was in the tree. It could not get down. Sarah went up in the tree and took the cat down. The cat was happy it could run and play again.

---

What is the main idea?

(A) **Sarah helped a cat.**

(B) **A cat ran away.**

"We have fun at school," said José. "We read and play games. I can see all my friends, too." José said good-by and ran to school.

---

What is the main idea?

(A) **José played a game.**

(B) **José likes school.**

Mother said, "We are going for a ride." The girls got into the car. They went to the zoo. They saw many animals there.

---

What is the main idea?

**(A) Mother took the girls to the zoo.**

**(B) Mother and the girls found a pet.**

Bill had lost his toy airplane. He looked all around the house, but he could not find it. Bill began to cry. He wanted his airplane.

What is the main idea?

**(A) Bill has many toys.**

**(B) Bill wanted his airplane.**

Ted has a pet bird that talks. It can say, "eat," "sleep," and "play." When Ted goes to school, the bird says, "good-by." Ted likes talking to his bird.

---

What is the main idea?

**(A) Ted has an old bird.**

**(B) Ted has a bird that talks.**

Rosa saw something in the grass. She went over to look. It was money. Rosa took the money home. She showed it to her mother.

What is the main idea?

(A) **Rosa found some money.**

(B) **Rosa has a little sister.**

Bob saw a little dog. The dog did not have a home. Bob took the dog home with him. Now he has a pet.

What is the main idea?

**(A) A dog ran away.**

**(B) Bob got a pet.**

Mother got into the car to go home. The car would not go. Mother got out of the car. She had to walk all the way home.

What is the main idea?

**(A) Mother got a new car.**

**(B) Mother had to walk home.**

## A. Exercising Your Skill

Read the story in Unit 45 and look at the picture carefully. Find the main idea in the story. On your paper, answer the questions below.

1. Who went for a ride?
2. Where did the family go?
3. What did they do there?
4. Give the story a name. The name should tell the main idea.

## B. Expanding Your Skill

Put the words in the box into two lists. Write a name for each list.

| | | |
|---|---|---|
| cow | tiger | elephant |
| monkey | pig | goat |

## C. Exploring Language

Read each sentence. Write the missing letters on your paper. Give the story a name. The name tells the main idea.

1. I love the _oo!
2. There are many _nimals to see.
3. I love to hear the roar of the _ions.
4. The _iraffe is easy to spot.
5. I love to watch the _eals at play.

## D. Expressing Yourself

Do one of these things.

1. Ask your classmates about their favorite animals at the zoo. Ask them why they like that animal the best.

2. With a friend or by yourself, draw a map of a make-believe zoo. Be sure to show homes for your favorite animals. Use a large piece of paper. Give your map a name.

3. Draw a picture of your favorite animal at home in a zoo. Give your picture a name.